FIRST STORY

CHANGING LIVES THROUGH WRITING

First Story changes lives through writing.

There is dignity and power in telling our own story. We help disadvantaged young people find their voices.

First Story places professional writers into secondary schools serving low-income communities, where they work intensively with students and teachers to foster confidence, creativity and writing ability.

Our programmes expand young people's horizons and raise aspirations. Students gain vital skills that underpin their success in school and support their transition to further education and employment.

To find out more and get involved, go to www.firststory.org.uk.

First Story is a registered charity number 1122939 and a private company limited by guarantee incorporated in England with number 06487410. First Story is a business name of First Story Limited.

First published 2019 by First Story Limited
Omnibus Business Centre, 39–41 North Road, London, N7 9DP

www.firststory.org.uk

ISBN 978-0-85748-369-0

1 3 5 7 9 10 8 6 4 2

A CIP catalogue record for this book is available from the British Library.

Printed and bound in the UK by Aquatint
Typeset by Avon DataSet Ltd
Copyedited by Hannah Aston
Proofread by Camille Ralphs
Cover designed by Kate Kunac-Tabinor

The Eight Dimensions of Easton

An Anthology by the First Story Group
at City Academy Bristol

Edited by Chris Redmond | 2019

As Patron of First Story I am delighted that it continues to foster and inspire the creativity and talent of young people in secondary schools serving low-income communities.

I firmly believe that nurturing a passion for reading and writing is vital to the health of our country. I am therefore greatly encouraged to know that young people in this school – and across the country – have been meeting each week throughout the year in order to write together.

I send my warmest congratulations to everybody who is published in this anthology.

Camilla

HRH The Duchess of Cornwall

Contents

What We're Up Against

History

Imaginings

We, the Philosophers

Introduction

Chris Redmond, Writer-in-Residence

It takes courage to show up
every week and write a little of yourself,
like it takes courage to stand
at the front of a classroom, smiling.
Music fans, Maths geeks,
Chicken-shop philosophers;
courage flaps the wings
of a flock of Easton eagles
flying into the wind
even when a storm
is boiling the air.

Over the autumn of 2018 and spring of 2019, I had the pleasure of working with the courageous writers of City Academy Bristol. At first I think they eyed me with suspicion. *Who is this be-hatted bloke coming into our library and robbing us of our Wednesday afternoons?* I was impressed immediately. One should always be suspicious. Suspicion provokes big questions of those courageous enough to ask them.

There are some great characters in this group: big personalities, always with a quip, a funny answer, a curve-ball perspective; quiet personalities who, after barely raising an eyebrow for weeks, offered up extraordinary, crafted lines which captured a moment or a feeling beautifully; and unusual personalities, completely surprising everyone with wild wordplay and wit that had us all laughing and scratching our heads. This is a group of writers, for sure.

For me, a good poem is like a coiled snake, a trip to the

circus or a hammer on emergency glass. It has to be urgent or tender or insightful or laugh-out-loud funny. Otherwise it's just functional language – business as usual. Poetry needs to be more than that. It's not just an exercise. It's an attempt to capture something human, messy and uncaptureable. When done well, it's alchemy.

This anthology is a record of some brave, honest, risky alchemic explorations. It's split into six sections. This wasn't planned. The poems and stories just sort of formed huddles of their own, so it made sense that they should hang out together.

The first section, **What You Mean to Me**, is a look under the lid of relationships: personal, familial, and imagined. It's deep in places and uncomfortable. Gabriella Sibanda's 'Reptile Skin' is a great example:

> I see how she shelters her heart in snake skin
> and braces against the world.

It's also funny, because relationships are, aren't they? Iqra Wasim's 'Cliché' for example.

> Daisies are pretty
> Daffodils have style
> Can you leave now?
> You've been here a while.

The second section, **A Place I Call...** is a collection of writing that explores the theme of home. It ranges from the real and humorous, from Jay Bryant,

> The smell of Dad's barbecue, ruined
> by my older brother's urge for the loo.

… to a heartbreaking and imagined story by Mariam Ali, that gives me a kick in the guts every time I read it.

What We're Up Against – the third section – takes a long, hard look at the road ahead, and the voices within that determine how we want to navigate it. There are some powerful images here. Whether it's Selaymon Wahidi comparing terrorism to a 'an isolated wasteland', or Noushima Mahamod describing the end of a the world as a 'hidden symphony', it's a strong section, with both a political voice and a sense of honest personal enquiry running throughout.

In **History** we have a selection of pieces written in response to a trip to Bristol's M-Shed museum, and a walk past the gates of Bristol's old jail, where public hangings took place. There are several poems that imagine hangings and a murder from different perspectives. We learned about eighteen-year-old Jon Horwood, who was hanged for killing sixteen-year-old Eliza Balsom after she rejected his advances. He wrote poetry in prison before he was executed. Our teacher-writer John Griffin also contributes a great poem to this section, capturing the intensity one of Bristol's most important riots.

The penultimate section, **Imaginings**, is a bold gaggle of pieces, exploring imagined scenarios and relationships. Dementia, suicide and eye transplants are just some of the topics here. The section also includes the prize-winning hundred-word story, 'Untitled' by Sonika Bishop, which tells of a girl pining for summer while walking through a frozen park.

The final section is called **We, the Philosophers**. These are the poems and stories that look up and wonder. Ozair Ali finishes with hope and inspiration from the cosmos in his poem 'Fog':

Feel the universe's gaze
It's right that we take courage from stardust from time to time.

It's a fitting way to wrap things up.

The anthology is bookended by two group pieces, written by the eight writers of this book and several others who joined the workshops, but who didn't manage to see it though. We wanted to include something from them in the book because they too helped shaped the conversations, the poems and the directions of travel. And what directions. Multi-dimensional travel. That's what's in this book. Past, present, future, inside, outside and a whole load of the less-easy-to-explain-difficult-funny stuff that makes us who we are.

All hail, the bold, the brave, the beautiful *Eight Dimensions of Easton*.

Teacher's Foreword

John Griffin, English Teacher

First Story, in its second year at City Academy Bristol, began on a dull, rainy afternoon in September. A small group of intelligent students scattered around the Discovery Centre, unsure and tentatively waiting for it to begin. Who would have thought that six months later we would have this wonderfully eclectic collection of poems? An anthology that the students can be proud of. An anthology to be cherished.

The students have flourished and developed on this course. I witnessed them become more confident and creative, not only in their writing, but as individuals too. From the hesitance and uncertainty in those early sessions – which were filled with nervous laughter – to the latter sessions where these new poets found their voices and read their work with assurance.

Unleashing latent or long-dormant creativity is no easy task. Chris Redmond, our Writer-in-Residence, teased and encouraged this from the students – with apparent ease – through a range of engaging activities that began with them exploring their identities. Following this, the group wrote a collaborative piece (included in this anthology under the title 'I Am') where it quickly became evident that there was an obsession with curry – especially biryani – and fast food in general. This light-hearted poem revealed a lot about the personalities in the group and some of the themes reappear in individual pieces later. From thinking of ourselves as a metaphor, Chris guided us into a realm of looking at everything as a metaphor. I remember asking Chris myself, after one session, whether he thought it possible to think in metaphors. He assured me, with a smile and a nod, that it is and he does. It is safe to say that the students all live, breathe, think and probably dream metaphors now – me included. I am thankful to Chris for this linguistic enlightenment.

Evidence of this shift in thinking and writing was noticeable right from the start. The students have each included three kennings about themselves as a unique mini-biography. Read them and wonder a little about each author – look for a clue as to what will be revealed about them and their writing in this collection.

As well as the poetry, students also wrote and practised a range of prose-writing. We wrote challenging six-word stories, aiming to include hints of plot, character and theme. After this, the students were given more words to play with, writing for the First Story 100-Word Story Competition. It was enjoyable to read these strong pieces and observe how the students were becoming more thoughtful in their word choice and use of language to create imagery. The prizewinning story is included in this anthology.

The students deserve praise for their commitment to the programme, giving up their own time after school on a weekly basis over the past six months. This small group showed a real willingness to learn and develop over this time. Perhaps this was best exemplified by their seven-hour writing session during the school day, towards the end of the project. With little need to be cajoled, the students sat and typed, talked about and tinkered with their words over this long day. By the end of it we were all exhausted. The work that came out of it, though, is very special and is a culmination of everything they have put into this experience – which is their all.

I am proud of them, and of this anthology. I hope you read it, share it, savour and enjoy it. I hope all the poets featured in it will continue to write and look at the world around them through the lens of a metaphor.

I Am

The First Story Group

I am an accident-prone golden child
I am 5'8"
A very creative, curious tiger
I am long black hair
I am a blank canvas
I am a computer
Which can craft curry in a 3 x 3 grid
I am an empty park at 2 a.m.
I am my own inner demon
I am Easton Takeaway
I am chips
I am roti and salan
A plate of dhal
I am extensions and braids
I am sunset on the horizon
I am a cancer
I am a capricorn
I am a taurus
I am a nerd
I am a blue blanket
A black sofa and curry
I am braces and Chelsea boots
I am my phone and a black metal chair
I am autumnal decorations
Like the different coloured leaves
And dark nights
I am a sister
I am a pair of shoes I've had since I was in Year Eight

I am my computer and Counterstrike
I am a day out at the beach
I am fun
I am a martial artist
I am content

What You Mean to Me

Reptile Skin

Gabriella Sibanda

They ask me why I love her,
Spend so much time with her;
They don't understand that she's a part of me now.

They don't hear the loneliness in her scars whimper
as her compressed cries sleep deep in her heart.

But I see how she shelters her heart in snake skin
and braces against the world. Confusion sails
at some part of me but I know she runs in my blood now.

I'll keep her safe, because
I have to be the final version of happiness she knows.

The Murder of the Word Beginning with B

Gabriella Sibanda

Beauty:
Mama told him, Papa told him, Aunty, Uncle told him

that he was beautiful.

Then he left childhood behind and walked into reality,
walked into disaster.

He went to secondary school.

Cliché

Iqra Wasim

Roses are red
Violets are blue
Been talking for a while
But only about you

Lilies are white
Purple ones are rare
My mirror's behind me
And that's why you stare

Anemone grows
Buds like eggs
Your dog is hairy
And so are your legs

Foxgloves in bushes
Surrounding farms
The air is saucy
And so are your arms

Daisies are pretty
Daffodils have style
Can you leave now?
You've been here a while.

Familiar Face

Ozair Ali

The gust of wind that blows between you and me,
where did it find the loneliness it carries?
Your face shines and glows in the night hue.
You look at me in disgust;
My realisation shoots into the sky and showers me with tears.
I know what you give me.
All I want you to do is leave
your translucent smile, obey what you truly feel.
When you come back, our eyes will make a sign;
The stars will align to make our eyes glow.
It will ache in my core just to see your familiar face.

Blossom Rain

After Miraie and Keio

Ozair Ali

Rain rolled off my hoodie.
The bright hue enlightened me.
Engulfed me.
Bliss might sneak into the spring.
Into your heart.
Pink flowing petals fall gracefully to the ground
Like every blossom rain does.

An Unresponsive Soul

Jay Bryant

I don't know why he won't talk, or even socialise. I get that it's better to be a lone wolf, but you can't always do everything yourself. This boy is impassive, he walks in a perfect straight line, no diversity, and never moves his mouth during… well… anything. Not even for lunch. He never responds to any questions hurled directly at him. I don't understand it. It's almost like he's an unresponsive soul.

Lost

Iqra Wasim

This poem is filled with words
I can't muster the courage to utter.
I may have been scared, but you
were the biggest coward of all.
Main character in a movie,
partnered with an extra.
That is not how it has ever been.
Always the princess and prince,
the king and queen.
I get that fire only thrives with gasoline.
You wanted someone innocent,
someone new,
and my innocence withered
with every person it took to get to you.
Last year I would have said,
'I miss you,' but
how could I say anything has changed?
When time goes backwards
whenever I hear your name.

Of All the Pretty Horses

After Cormac McCarthy and inspired by Post Malone's 'Fall Apart'

Gabriella Sibanda

You're seductively dark,
evil, twisted,
a taste of sweet venom,
a demon disguised as my angel.
You're dark like the night sky
eerily illuminating my life like stars are supposed to
as you chant those honey lies,
'I love you, always', and trap me again
under your spell. Like a fool,
I run back to you. Again
and again, you leave me stranded.

Peering Right Through Me

Gabriella Sibanda

Dark skies,
like her soul,
with ocular planets planted
where her eyes were; she
stared
into me.

Buried Under Flowers

Noushima Mahamod

If there's one thing I've learnt it's that we all heal.
I know this because the moon told me so.
One way or another,
It takes time. I should know;
Our hearts soothed and minds repaired,
Distant memories of sadness
Now buried under flowers.

The Fall

Ozair Ali

How do I look from above?
I'm all alone on a mountaintop
Because you climbed up high to the endless sky.
Nobody can answer me; no one can follow me.
Why, you ask? I've broken ties.
The cold itself begs for warmth,
The warmth of your smile.
You drift away, further and further.
Why not come down?
If you're happy up there,
you've not hurt anyone – other than yourself.
I've just been pushed to the darkness below.

Cringey Puns

Iqra Wasim

You said you needed time
So I gave you a watch.

You said you needed space
So I gave you the universe.

You said you needed a break
So I gave you lunch.

You said you needed 100%
So I gave you my charger.

You wanted my support
So I gave you my bra.

So many fans,
You still aired me.

You gave me a ruler
But I wasn't straight.

Thanks

Ozair Ali

I can't say it enough but thank you.
Tomorrow can't be seen but I know
you will be the most loving soul around.
You haven't changed
and for that,
I can't thank you enough.

A Place I Call…

Home

Jay Bryant

Home is a hub of annoyances and tragedy
filled with: a mum's yelling, drowned out
by my cousin's cringe-summoning dancing;
a lack of sleep; siblings
chucking me out of my room. Outside
is where horror looms:
tortured into Sunday chores;
dressed in hand-me-downs;
the busy bathroom groans.
The smell of Dad's barbecue, ruined
by my older brother's urge for the loo.

Home

Ozair Ali

Home is knowing who's coming up the stairs by how heavy the footsteps are.
Am I in trouble or am I in the clear?
A busy bathroom reminding me of bustling city life.
Oversized hand-me-downs that create clinging emotion.
But what about others?
What is home for them?
In war-torn countries, home is as good as gone,
home is a shadow of a peaceful past.
Home may be gunfire and planes screeching past.
Everyone's home is different,
like every crackle from a fire.

Home

Gabriella Sibanda

Home smells like fresh flowers.
It creeps into your heart like a thief.

Home is children running around screaming,
playing, falling then crying, but also quiet
and warm blankets in front a fireplace
as you're cuddled up with hot chocolate.

Being home turns windy dark days
into blue warm skies, and it's everyone
being deluded, insane, and everyone
being okay with it.

Home, to me, tastes like sweet honey
or Nanny's rice and peas on Sunday.
It tastes like church patty after service
or jerk chicken in summer.

It brings the summery vibe
of going on holiday and fills your whole body
with happiness, caressing you
safely, like a baby.

Some refer to it as a place,
I say it's a feeling.
I carry home
wherever I go.

Home

Selaymon Wahidi

Home is laughter,
warmth and happiness,
the never-ending sound
of chatter and jokes, children running
up and down the corridors,
the smell of rice and khofta
engulfing the air when I return from school,
the sound of crying
when my brother loses his toy car.

Home is a haven,
where all problems vanish into an abyss,
a place to forget about outside.
A sanctuary, each home
is like a star in the sky.

Home

Sonika Bishop

Home is big red buses going up and down the street,
filled with people on adventures. Home
is watching the skyline of London through my kitchen window.
Home is going on spontaneous adventures with my mom,
old-time songs playing through the speakers

while I play in the yard.
Going to church on a Sunday.

Home is swinging under the mango tree.

Home

Mariam Ali

Years ago, a daughter asked her mum about home,
during a war which seemed like it wouldn't end.

'Home is more than just a house, sweetheart.'
She spoke reassuringly inside the false comfort of the air-raid
shelter,
which her innocent daughter believed wouldn't fail or falter
in its job of keeping them safe.

Her questioning eyes did not surprise the mother one bit,
for she knew her star was more than met the eye.

'One day, my child, you shall find a home,
whether you choose to have a family or venture through
life alone.'
She smiled and continued, hinting at her own experience,

'Whether you find sanctuary and comfort in someone's arms,
Just know that you can be someone's home too.'

The girl smiled hopefully.

'Regardless of where you come from, my dear,
just never fear
or forget my words,
that everyone will find a home,
including you.'

She gave a last kiss to her daughter's forehead, as she fell asleep
and slipped out of the shelter on silent feet,
her last prayer being that her daughter would find her
    safe haven
as she had found her own.

What We're Up Against

Left to Face the End of the World Alone

Noushima Mahamod

I want to capture it like thunder
that I can't escape, it exists
in the distance,
a hidden symphony
of treacherous fears.

Look What You Have Done!

Gabriella Sibanda

You're killing me, can't you see,
Poisoning every part of me.
Once we were joined, just called 'we',
Now we're separate, you and me.

What happened to the times we shared?
I birthed you, grew you literally out of me.
I gave you light and crops to eat;
We unified in harmony.

So why do you mercilessly murder me,
Destroy what I gave to thee,
War and sin on top of me,
Harm my core and slaughter me?

You litter into my deep blue eyes
And pollute my lands; I'm not surprised.
How could you all have been so blind?
To not see, you're causing yourself to die.

And now time is not so vast,
For you all to see your last,
As floods sweep in and diseases spread;
All of you will soon be dead.

And so it will just be me again:
Mother Nature – I wonder, shall I try again
To give mankind another chance,
When mankind's will to change is fake?
Can you learn from your mistakes?

War

Mariam Ali

A melancholy violin
played in a field of poppies,
smoky red, dull grey
storm clouds; worn-out uniforms dipped in death.
Whispers of remembrance, discussing the screams
heard for a quiet saviour, discarded,
unwanted. Families left
feeling lost, incomplete.
A limp figure staggering, stumbling
to a place where they can be at peace.
A blank canvas, nothing left
to show what they had gone through.

It wouldn't be a piano
played for wealthy folk,
not the colour of bright yellow,
worn to express joy.
It wouldn't be a warm sunny day,
not a dress or a new jacket.
It wouldn't be the sound of laughter
echoing after a good joke,
a bubbly, contagious sound
spreading through a room,
not the feeling of happiness, contentment
or safety. It wouldn't be
the family dinner on a Sunday.
It wouldn't be colours.

Terrorism

Selaymon Wahidi

A rusty harmonica
Grey-brown and awfully dull
Thunder and rain in an isolated area
A vest
A deep voice, quite grumpy
Believe or suffer with everyone else
Speaking under its breath
Full of anger and hatred
Fast and urgently walking
An isolated wasteland
A dark picture, a huge blur.

Bravery

Selaymon Wahidi

He is the one, quiet
in a crowd of people cheering.
He is never out of place.
Quick thinker, no instruction manual,
self-defensive; a wall of his own around him.
Hides his unusual thoughts
messing up his haunted brain.
Mind corrupted, can't be fixed.
He is scared,
not a moment of safety.
He is threatened,
but managing to fight it
and bare it all.
He is brave.

National Women's Day

For Tomi Lahren – Trump supporter

Noushima Mahamod

Well Lahren, today we are women,
strong and fiercely empowered,
eyes so full of life,
dictated by curiosity,
never a silent moment
or a dull sound.
Things are brighter when we love,
warmer when we speak
and better when we *are.*

Destitution

Iqra Wasim

He is a rusty whistle
imitating a slow death.
He is the smell of petrichor, still lingering
in a thick coat, husky,
sore and deep, he repeats
please and thank you
in the day, hoping
for comfort at night, quiet,
insecure, limping,
a sense of heaviness. His home:
an alleyway, a plethora
of grey, white and black.

He isn't a piano
played in the largest of halls.
He isn't pink, like the dolls
little girls play with; his voice
is not high-pitched, full of energy.
He does not say 'I am at peace'.
He is not walking with pride or joy.
His voice is not confident.
His residence is not a castle.
He is only one bad choice

from being my self-portrait.

Things I No Longer Wish to Understand

Mariam Ali

I no longer wish to understand
why we call ourselves humans; we stroll around
throwing humanity under the bus, casually
watching people suffer.

It's sickening how
we're so used to seeing
the news about war; another country,
a diabolical plan brewing, monsters
caring for nothing.
Destruction,
without a glance back.

What have we become? My voice
is drowned by people who believe
they're creating a better world, progress measured
by nuclear power plants built.
Not the saved tree, some place
where suffering and pain doesn't exist.

Calling this destruction of the environment
'a work in progress', is deranged,
when everyone's eyes turn blindly. Nothing
has changed. We ignore the cold,
hard, bittersweet of it all.

Future generations of kids
will never know the Amazon rainforest,

won't know the rare animals
that roamed the land,
or how people visited the beach
to watch the tide wash away the sand.
Maybe that generation will see us as
'the failures',
'Nature's experiments',
'the ones who got it wrong'.

That's not how I want to be remembered,
but do I have a choice?
You can call me short-tempered,
but I'm not okay
with just standing around
watching my world tear apart
and crash to the ground.
These are the things I no longer wish to understand.

What We Are Up Against

Gabriella Sibanda

It is not a calm flute humming.
It's not the colour of sense.
It is not a day of peace.
Its voice is not soothing, like waves
crusading through the wind; it screams
like a hundred shouting people in a small room.

It's a sunny day with soft rain.
It whispers, simultaneously shouting,
'YOU'RE CONFUSED AS TO WHAT YOU WANT!'
It hums the sweet melodies of a piano,
mixing high and low notes, the colours
of yellow,
orange,
purple.

Destiny

Jay Bryant

How the world has changed,
The weakest in it being caged;
Political corruption and international poverty,
But maybe… changing all this is my destiny.
Banish this virus from the edges of the earth
Or we'll see defections,
See the world around us burn.
Look around.
These structures are given to us,
Yet they are being replaced
By hoverboards, green engines
And solar panels.

Maybe I'm triggered or something,
But the concepts will just melt away.
The next generation can change this:
It's our destiny.
It's my destiny.

Tired

Noushima Mahamod

Tiredness:
it is a
snow-white violin,
a heavy snowstorm
calmingly deep, a raspy whisper,
maybe a strong craving
for serenity,
a warm bedroom in a cottage with big windows
framing the snowstorm outside.
It is air conditioning, a warm bed, a fireplace,
a painting; a night forest glowing with butterflies and flowers,
the moon's reflection on a pond, a fairy sat at the brink.

It isn't:
a sunny day on a beach in the Maldives;
a flowy dress dancing with the wind;
saying 'Go for it';
a nice dinner on the beach at night;
an explosion of bright colours.

Politics

Selaymon Wahidi

Politics is overrated
Nearly everything is debated
Most politicians are hated
But some of them are just fine
I don't really get politics
It's a whole waste of time

History

Broken Doll – Part One

Mariam Ali

A moment of realisation and regret for John Horwood, who accidentally killed Eliza Balsum after she rejected him – Bristol – 1821.

She lies in my arms, limp and soundless, without a pulse to connect her to this world. Her chestnut locks are a halo around her heart-shaped face, her eyelashes are resting on her warm skin, which is cooling against me. She is moving away. Unwillingly. Because of me. I can hear her laughter drowning now in a sleep so deep no cure will bring her back. When I threw that stone, for a second, I wanted her to feel the pain I had felt from her rejection. But now I hold her, just wishing.

Imagining the Hanging of Sarah Harriet Thomas, Aged Seventeen

Noushima Mahamod

Sarah Harriet Thomas was the last person to be hanged at Bristol New Gaol in 1849.

When the mind no longer bears sanity
everything comes crumbling, unfamiliar
a buried vibration, adrenaline
racing for the last time, unsettling
panic. Peace, yet nothing peaceful
in the final moments before the noose
and amongst the glaring eyes of the crowd,
you forget what to fear, intrigued,
eyes drenched in pity. Noose
now two seconds from your neck,
accepting death; more thoughts
than you can fathom. A heart-
shattering innocent-soul scream, messy
hair and a perfectly porcelain face dressed
in tears, fighting death like a warrior, left
to battle the world alone.

Final Destination: Jail

Sonika Bishop

Standing tall, I left the place I stayed most of my life: jail. Huge dirty cells trapped me from the outside world. It wasn't my fault. I was in the wrong place at the wrong time. Historical attraction, some call it, but I call it Hell. It's being replaced by a 'fresh start'. But what they have forgotten is that lives were ended. People gathered in the streets with an array of emotions scattered on their faces, waiting for my beheading. I opened my eyes one last time, to see my mother with a twisted smile on her face. That's when I realised: I had been set up.

Bristol Bridge 1793

John Griffin

He walks on to the bridge of betrayal, up to those grim gates.
Oh well, tolls can be dodged and gates can be burned.
Joyous shouts from the harbour walls, mood right for
the masses.
Barrels of beer, like draughts of courage, bonfires light up
the gates
like hellfire grills, crimson orange in the autumn light.
Table of tolls, gates burned down; this is the fight, he says.

Rewards pinned up on the new gates: offenders will pay.
Back on the bridge, Saturday night mischief and beer.
Crowds make their way, bringing faggots of wood from
Welshback, a ready-made bonfire stack.
Hundreds now frozen, enthralled by the sight,
silhouettes of blood-red figures face the light. In come
the magistrates, the militia, volleys of stones, screams
and shrieks.
Shoved forward, chaos rains – enough – forewarned,
Riot act read.

Back on the bridge, he walks up to the gates
barring the way. A new mob gathers, furious and defiant,
making a mess of this day of rest. Black night closes in.
Faint glows of warm orange, harbour wall; the mob grows,
watching carriages pass toll-free, overseen by the militia.
Tension heavy in the night, shattered by a gun-blast bullet,
and a man falls. John Abbott crawls home, cobbles
bloodstained,

wet red. Died on Temple Street,
feet from home.

Death bridge, militia stained, tainted by blood taken from
the innocent. Vengeance and anger, the mob comes,
tolls taken by blade, a sword in the face, brutal rule.
Chaff and banter against the gates. Riot act read. Regardless,
the mob comes, toll houses stormed. Soldiers retreat for
  the night.
Down the river flaming beacons of anarchy, justice, what's
  right.

But this time the blaze brought them back. An officer, eight
  men,
right off taking flack, fires out, a passing storm? Black night
returns. A drum beat breaks the peace, the fight
back on, the beat to arms, a pulse like a stolen hum.
Babes in arms, women, fathers all now come to see the gates
Ablaze – shouting, cheering, jeering.

The boiling night, flames lighting the river red, smoke a shroud
concealing the chaos. Soldiers in lines, marching to a different
  beat
down the High Street, hidden from light in the black shadows
of the harbour wall. An oyster shell, a rock thrown into the
  lines,
a soldier falls. 8.15 p.m., like a domino toppled, the response:
Bullets fired into the crowds, loud screams and shouts,
nowhere to run. Side streets blocked like drains in a storm,
  people
pushed back, spilling out into the bullets, cut down in
  an instant.

Street after street turned red, blood down into the river, red
from the blaze; last gasps of breath, a window smashed,
bullet intrudes splintering into the bed headboard. No time,
no warning, bodies motionless.
Those innocent of evil.

Broken Doll – Part Two

Mariam Ali

The story of John Horwood, who accidentally killed Eliza Balsum, continues…

My new home is behind thick pillars of steel,
Separating me from the world
where I chose to kneel for the girl
I believed was meant for me,
but I wasn't her cup of tea.

Irony,
don't you think?
I imagined laughable scenarios
where this wouldn't be my fate,
but rage washed through
and before I knew,
it was too late: dead
in my arms
she lay, peaceful
angelic features,
a porcelain figure,
in the hands of the worst of creatures.

I couldn't stand not having her.
Anger transformed me into a beast,
an unintentional killer,
mind dipped in despair,
fear clawing at my heart,
clouding thoughts with questions:

what can I do?
Well, not much now,
trapped in brick walls,
stained with blood – all sorts,
scratched initials;
I add mine too.
Time will come
I'll walk through the gates,
meet death, face to face,
but for now I sit,
isolated, writing
poetry behind bars.

Imaginings

Tom at Eighty Years Old: Dementia

Gabriella Sibanda

Why am I remembering this now?
Five years old, going to the park
Dad swinging me around.
We had ice cream that day.
That was such a long time ago
But now it's getting cloudy.
What am I doing?
Ah yes, tea.
Where did I put the tea bags?
Claire will know.
'Claire?'
No answer.
'Claire?'
Perhaps she's putting Holly to sleep.
I'll go upstairs, and check in Holly's room.
It looks deserted, as though no one's been here for years.
But that's not right. Holly was home from school yesterday.
Dingdong!
I'll open that.
Who's this?
Claire? Holly?
It looks like Holly but much, much older.
And a child?
'Grandpa!'
Grandpa?!
This isn't right.
Again: 'Pa?'
The girl who looks like Holly asks.

‘Who are you? Where’s Claire?’
‘Pa, calm down. Ma’s dead. Has been for five years now.’
‘Claire? Dead? Nonsense!’
What’s wrong with me? I keep forgetting things.
Where are my car keys?
What day is it?
How old am I?
What was I doing again?
Ah yes, tea.

Honesty

Jay Bryant

Honesty is a middle-class man in Newcastle,
dressed up in a fancy suit, listening to relaxing music.
He wants a job, desperately, as he sips his tea.
He wants to support a dying friend of his
so, Honesty opens up his suitcase, ready for the interview.
He tells the interviewer his strengths
and weaknesses, his dying friend,
but bringing up such a topic breaks Honesty down.
Where others would lie, Honesty is true to his name.
He runs towards home, turns off the relaxing music
and lies down in agony.
Later, Honesty is commended
for revealing his true motives, praised
for always telling the truth.
So he tries again and comes clean about that day.
The interviewer feels sympathetic
and gives him the job.
Honesty, although full of grief, now has support
and he has learnt a life lesson.
What separated him from anyone else was his weakness,
but it was also his strength.

Untitled

Sonika Bishop

Consumed by her thoughts, she wanders through the park, green leaves now white. The air cold and sharp. Goosebumps on her skin. The warm, cloudless sky, a figment of her imagination. Warmth, nothing but a memory – of the next-door neighbour's barbecue, of the sweet melody of the ice cream van, wearing crop-tops underneath the scorching sun.

A harsh slap from winter brought her back, back to the bitter reality of gloomy short days, windows closed to create a warm home, being swallowed in jackets and scarves. Summer, she could see it – but would she ever feel it again?

Papa's Last Song

Gabriella Sibanda

Mama said 'life's a lie'
When Papa stopped and took his life.

'I waited for the day,' he'd sighed.
'The day the voices would go away.'

And now it comes back to me,
what he said.
'Problems aren't really demons under your bed.
It's the ones that prosper inside your head.
The ones who claw and scratch inside your brain
and slither and steal all precious memories away,
because like the devil, they manipulate
And screech at you to do things you hate
And medication doesn't work,' he cried,
'they told me that. It's all just lies.'

So he took us to that suspension bridge
and I watched as off the side he hinged
and as he looked back,
I saw freedom in his eyes.

The Cliffside

Ozair Ali

I've just been left here in the swaying luscious grass.
Stars await my response.
I stare up and admire their beauty.
Do they know how I feel?
The silky flowing blades comforting me
one after another.

Moon appears from behind clouds.
It gleams hopefulness. I don't take it.
I shun it and peer into nothingness.

The sea ripples calmly, soothes my problems.
A sorrowful breeze passes, waving
calamity at all this peace. Sea erupts,
lashing at the cliff base, moon hides,
stars dim, then slowly
another moonflower blooms,
soothing me, a gift.
I accept, lie back
and tranquillity returns.
I look into the blushing sunrise.

Stolen Goods

Mariam Ali

I've been a thief all my life,
or that's what I told myself
once I knew
that the things I use to see
were not always a part of me;
donated, to replace
the ones that didn't function
properly. The eyes

I look through now
are the softest of browns,
infused with hues of vibrant green,
gracefully laced around irises
of borrowed orbs. Now
I see the world through her eyes.

I visited her grave today,
once I found out her name.
I live with her memories, life
will never be the same,
so it would have been a shame
if I hadn't ever gone to see her
and give my thanks
for all these stolen goods.

Sleephorrors

Gabriella Sibanda

Have you ever seen your own child lowered into the ground?
Felt your whole world freeze?
As if time wanted to play a game and trap you forever.
Well, God played a joke on me that day –
I'll tell you that – as I watched them
lower my baby into the earth.

Back into the universe but away from me.

And no matter how much I scream and curse,
he's not coming back.

The Eyes I Dream In

Ozair Ali

The vast sea you behold.
Many come and go.
The colours switch and the pirate ships disappear.
The dips, climbs and lack of sleep
make, always, dreams of sheep.
The relay of these images
better than any camera can see.
The swell of sweetness.
Brown eyes, brown toes
red ears, red nose.
The holes in my skin make me whole.
The spots come and go.
Running strong, my sharp thin *katanas*
make some holes.
As my fatigue is captured,
the emerald repels as many come, many throw.
The sea's crispy detail will help,
delve deeper.
Just watch the truth unfold
of the vast green hue you behold.

We, the Philosophers

Dream Lantern

(Original song title by RADWIMPS)

Ozair Ali

It lights up the way.
Never-ending stories lie in my path.
Picking up this lantern awakens everything.
Looking over the growth of crowds in my life,
one thing stands out. The strength of souls
and frailty of tears. Everyone says
there's nothing certain in this world
but we've got hope right here, y'know.

Change of Heart

Noushima Mahamod

The way the wind appeared
for a brief moment
has given my molten heart
a change of mood
and left some pleasant parts
of a day I thought I had rued.

The Tear That Falls from My Left Eye

Ozair Ali

It is a piano sat happily in a hatchback, ready to drop anytime.
But not a drum-set cabled down to earth.
It shines blue, highlighting the tear's frailty, ready to imitate
 the sky's endlessness.
It just can't be red.
It just screams death.
The pink highlights present sakura petals
gracefully falling; the suit ready to drop it,
but it isn't dying plants on a sunny day while naked,
the empty voice trembling at the fear of cold.
It's not going to be screaming at the top if its lungs, loving
 the heat.
The random afternoon that lies here unfolds an insecure voice.
The planned morning routine that is ready to go uploads a
 confident bellow.
The voice fuelling a fast walk – a walk to be unnoticed.
The voice fuelling a mediocre jog – a flash of attention-seeking.
The crowded forest that lies untouched for centuries
holds a power to shine on command. The sun, with no plan
 to stop,
pierces small holes held by the trees, dormant for someone to
 step inside.
Instead, it rains when I enter its vicinity.
Am I a sad machine
supplying depression?
Its picture is a whole day of shade.
Highlight and undo.

A Cloudy and Shady Memory

Jay Bryant

I could've stopped that train-wreck, but didn't.
I've been told to relax, but memories of that day
won't stop invading. They're infecting me
everywhere: in school, at home, even in the park.
I wade through sadness and grief like a swamp, guilt
waiting for me around every corner like a mafia boss.
Friends ask, 'What's wrong?'
but I can't bring myself to open that chamber.
These memories hurt me. Every day,
a fragment of me changes. At this point,
I just want to fade away…
because souls can fade,
but memories can't.

(Advice from) the Creature under the Bed

Mariam Ali

'There's beauty in simplicity,' it said,
'Forget whatever they say,
The colour brown
Shouldn't bring you down
When they compare it with something like grey.'

'Flowers bloom,' it reminded me,
'Throughout the seasons too.
Grass is green,
And summer is lean,
So you should not be blue.'

'Your eyes aren't brown,' it reassured,
'They're dipped in honey with sage.
Fragile copper orbs,
Which glow when they water;
Trapped emotions in a cage.'

'Your actions will leave a mark,' it whispered.
'On the hearts of those you surround.
They'll know you tried,
Failed or survived,
With your promises you are bound.'

'When words cannot be used,' it stated,
'To describe how you're their muse,
Just know, young one,
You've conquered them all,
So do not be confused.'

‘Wipe those tears.’ (Its last words spoken.)
‘Take my advice and sleep.
Wake in the morning
With a clear mind,
Knowing that beauty isn’t only skin deep.’

Fog

Ozair Ali

Close your eyes.
Feel the universe's gaze;
it's right that we take courage from stardust from time to time.
Right?
On the deepest of darkest nights,
on the highest of highs,
I try to get a head start on a dream,
get cold at 3 a.m.
Sometimes the five dimensions keep teasing me.
I don't know my way,
but stars, peering in on my thoughts, guide me.
I just carry on.

I Am Too

The First Story Group

I am Asian
Dark hair and dark eyes
I am biryani
Strength with spice
I am an Easton Takeaway £2.50 meal
I am plain naan bread
I am my bed and a tonne of fruit
I am blazer and a tie
I am short and a hijab
I am a warm fuzzy blanket
A white fluffy coat
I am school trousers and Armani jumper
Earrings and false nails
I am a machine that runs along rails
I am a phone that hates being charged
I am my bed and Netflix –
An insomniac
I am dog-bite scars on my arm
A gymnast
A swimmer
A hugging koala
I am one who commits to a translucent smile
I am Jamaica
I am one in a million

Six-Word Biographies

Ozair Ali: Formal penguin, shallow depth, pen controller.

Mariam Ali: Cake maker, fruit lover, star gazer.

Selaymon Wahidi: Biryani boy, ten-toed poet, indecisive debt.

Iqra Wasim: Side-splitter, joke peddlar, walking anecdote.

Jay Bryant: Total outcast, stress endurer, secret conniver.

Sonika Bishop: Story whisperer, metaphor harbour, wry smiler.

Gabriella Sibanda: Beam machine, light shiner, poem hatcher.

Noushima Mahamod: Wise-cracker, time hustler, deep diver.

Chris Redmond (Writer-in-Residence): Song hunter, word wrangler, crisp enthusiast.

John Griffin (Teacher): Beard champion, biscuit boss, camouflaged novelist.

With additional contributions from Tony Tran, Reshum Kaur and Amelia Begum.

Acknowledgements

Melanie Curtis at Avon DataSet for her overwhelming support for First Story and for giving her time in typesetting this anthology.

Hannah Aston for copy-editing this anthology and supporting the project.

Kate Kunac-Tabinor and all the designers at Oxford University Press for their overwhelming support for First Story.

David Greenwood and Foysal Ali at Aquatint for printing this anthology at a discounted rate.

Bristol museums We The Curious and M Shed for allowing the students to visit and work on site for free.

The Dulverton Trust who supported First Story in this school.

HRH The Duchess of Cornwall, Patron of First Story.

Thanks to:
Arts Council England, Alice Jolly & Stephen Kinsella, Andrea Minton Beddoes & Simon Gray, The Arvon Foundation, BBC Children in Need, Beth & Michele Colocci, Blackwells, Boots Charitable Trust, Brunswick, Charlotte Hogg, Cheltenham Festivals, Clifford Chance, Dulverton Trust, Edith Murphy Foundation, First Editions Club Members, First Story Events Committee, Frontier Economics, Give A Book, Ink@84, Ivana Catovic of Modern Logophilia, Jane & Peter Aitken, John Lyon's Charity, John Thaw Foundation, Miles Trust for the Putney & Roehampton Community, Old Possum's Practical

Trust, Open Gate Trust, Oxford University Press, Psycle Interactive, Royal Society of Literature, Sigrid Rausing Trust, The Stonegarth Fund, Teach First, Tim Bevan & Amy Gadney, Walcot Foundation, Whitaker Charitable Trust, William Shelton Education Charity, XL Catlin, our group of regular donors, and all those donors who have chosen to remain anonymous.

Most importantly we would like to thank the students, teachers and writers who have worked so hard to make First Story a success this year, as well as the many individuals and organisations (including those who we may have omitted to name) who have given their generous time, support and advice.